Triumph Spitfire MkIV and Spitfire 1500 Parts List

MGL 6401

CONTENTS

Page No.

Engine	4
Mountings (Engine, Gearbox & Differential)	4
Oil Control	5
Engine Gaskets	5
Exhausts	5
Cooling	5
Clutch	6
Gearbox- Three Rail	6
Gearbox- Single Rail	6
Overdrive- D and J Type	6
Drive Train	7
Differential Unit	7
Fuel Systems	7
Steering	8
Steering Wheels	8
Front Suspension	8
Anti-Roll Bar	9
Rear Suspension	9
Brakes	9
Hand Brake	10
Distributor- Delco	10
Distributor- Lucas	10
Electrical Units	10
Switches	10
Lighting	11
Wipers & Washers	11
Control Cables	11
Road Wheels	11
Body	12
Door Fittings	13
Interior Trim	14
Badges & Brightwork	14
Body Rubber	15
Weather Equipment	15
Books	15
Accessories	15
Chassis & Engine No. Details	15

INTRODUCTION

This Parts List has been produced to highlight the major fast-moving components for the Triumph Spitfire MKIV and Spitfire 1500 that we stock. Whilst we have, for the last 8 years, sold an increasing number of parts for both these, and the earlier Spitfire, models it became clear to the company that many potential customers, perceiving us as only interested in the Triumph TR and MG range, did not realise the depth and breadth of our Spitfire stock-holding.

This listing is seen as very much a temporary measure, produced to fulfill a need whilst we continue work on a full catalogue which will encompass the entire Spitfire model range. As such, this Parts List does not list every component that we can supply from either stock or to special order. We therefore urge you, if you require a part not listed here, to not hesitate to telephone or contact by other methods any of the outlets listed below.

As this publication is primarily concerned with standard, original fitment, parts we have only listed a few of the numerous 'tuning' components that are available for the Triumph Spitfire from our sister division- TriumphTune, and listed in their Performance Manual. The TriumphTune staff in Richmond will be only too happy to help with any specific tuning enquiries that you may have. (For address/telephone details see below.)

ORDERING: We welcome visitors to our shops, and orders by letter, telephone,or fax on:

 Cox & Buckles Spares/TriumphTune: 22-28 Manor Rd. Richmond, Surrey TW9 1YB
Tel: 081 948 6666 (C&B) Tel: 081 948 6668 (TriumphTune)   Fax: 081 940 9268

 Cox & Buckles Spares, Midlands: 991 Wolverhampton Rd. Oldbury, West Midlands.
B69 4RT. Tel: 021 544 5555   Fax: 021 544 4340

 Sprite & Midget B, C, V8 Centre: 93 Newfoundland Rd. Bristol, Avon BS1 9LU
Tel: 0272 232523 Fax: 0272 428236

 Barry Stafford MG Parts Ltd: 113-115 Stockport Rd. Cheadle Heath, Stockport, Cheshire
SK3 0JE. Tel: 061 480 6402   Fax: 061 429 0349

 Naylor Brothers MG Parts Ltd: Regent House, Dockfield Rd. Shipley, W. Yorks BD17 7SF
Tel: 0274 594071   Fax: 0274 531149

 Moss Darlington: 15 Allington Way, Yarm Rd. Industrial Estate, Darlington, Co. Durham
DL1 4QB. Tel: 0325 281343 Fax: 0325 485563

EXPORT: All outlets can supply goods to overseas retail customers. We have a specialist Retail Export Department based at our Richmond premises, direct telephone number **081 948 8106**.

PAYMENT: Payment made by cash, personal cheque (up to the guarantee limit), certified bank draft. Access (Master Charge) and Visa credit cards are accepted and are particularly useful for telephone/fax ordering.

EXCHANGE UNITS & SURCHARGES: Certain items are available on an exchange basis only. In some cases, and applicable to all such units in the case of overseas sales, we may require that you supply a reconditionable old unit prior to despatch of the replacement. Please telephone for further details.

CARRIAGE/PACKING CHARGES: We use the most economic method available. For urgent orders/over-night delivery etc. please discuss with our telephone sales staff.

PRICES: Accompanying this Parts Lists is a price list current at the date of publication. As prices change regularly you are advised to contact our telephone sales staff at point of ordering to confirm the current price.

ENGINE

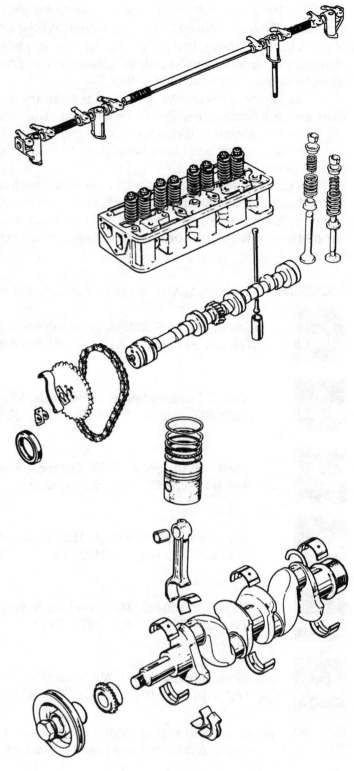

155907STD	4	Piston w/Rings (Standard)	1300 H/C
AEU2778	4	Piston w/Rings (.020")	1300 H/C
155907030	4	Piston w/Rings (.030")	1300 H/C
155907040	4	Piston w/Rings (.040")	1300 H/C
AE20139STD	4	Piston w/Rings (Standard)	1500 H/C
AE20139020	4	Piston w/Rings (.020")	1500 H/C
AE20139030	4	Piston w/Rings (.030")	1500 H/C
AE20139040	4	Piston w/Rings (.040")	1500 H/C
RTC1754	1	Big End Bearing Set (Standard)	1300/1500
RTC1754010	1	Big End Bearing Set (.010)	1300/1500
RTC1754020	1	Big End Bearing Set (.020)	1300/1500
RTC1754030	1	Big End Bearing Set (.030)	1300/1500
RTC1754040	1	Big End Bearing Set (.040)	1300/1500
RTC1753	1	Main Bearing Set (Standard)	1300/1500
RTC1753010	1	Main Bearing Set (.010)	1300/1500
RTC1753020	1	Main Bearing Set (.020)	1300/1500
RTC1753030	1	Main Bearing Set (.030)	1300/1500
RTC1753040	1	Main Bearing Set (.040)	1300/1500
AEW2171STD	1	Thrust Washer Set (Standard)	1300/1500
AEW2171005	1	Thrust Washer Set (.005)	1300/1500
AEW2171015	1	Thurst Washer Set (.015)	1300/1500
146454	4	Connecting Rod Assy.	1300/1500
119813	4	Small End Bearing	1300/1500
143552	8	Cam Followers	1300/1500
157508	8	Push Rod	1300/1500
144962	1	Rocker Shaft	1300/1500
144962B	1	Rocker Shaft (Repro)	1300/1500
109023	4	Rocker Arm (No. 1,3,5,7)	1300/1500
109024	4	Rocker Arm (No. 2,4,6,8)	1300/1500
UKC1427R	1	Exchange Cylinder Head w/Valves and Springs (1300 High Compression) (Engine No. FH25001HE Onwards)	
UKC1428R	1	Exchange Cylinder Head w/Valves and Springs (1300 Low Compression) (Engine No. FH25001LE Onwards)	
TKC1155XR	1	Exchange Cylinder Head w/Valves and Springs (1500 Twin Carb) (Engine No. FM28001HE Onwards)	
145328	4	Inlet Valve (Up to 1975)	1300/1500
UKC2460	4	Inlet Valve (1975 On)	1500
153886	4	Exhaust Valve (Up to 1975)	1300/1500
144965	4	Exhaust Valve (1975 On)	1500
136487	8	Valve Spring (Single Type)	1300
157229	8	Valve Spring Outer (Double)	1300/1500
157476	8	Valve Spring Inner (Double)	1300/1500
TT1307	1	Double Valve Springs, Engine Set	1300/1500
106663	16	Valve Cotters	1300/1500
105131	1	Timing Chain	1300/1500
042425	1	Timing Chain Tensioner	1300/1500
211126	1	Timing Cover Gasket	1300/1500
RKC3305E	1	Camshaft	1300/1500
036411	1	Cam Gear Locktab	1300/1500
UKC1110	1	Timing Cover Oil Seal	1300/1500
143456	1	Rear Engine Oil Seal	1300/1500
155357	1	Crank Pulley Nut	1300/1500

MOUNTINGS

UKC5334	2	Front Engine Mounting	MKIV/1500
CHA615	2	Gearbox Mounting (Non-O/D)	MKIV/1500
159656	1	Gearbox Mounting (O/D)	MKIV/1500
133568	2	Differential Mounting Upper	MKIV/1500
131796	2	Differential Mounting Lower	MKIV/1500
117578	2	Differential Mounting Rear	MKIV/1500
136869	1	Diff. Mounting Rear Bolt (Long)	MKIV/1500

moss | London 081 948 6666. Birmingham 021 544 5555. Bristol 0272 232523.

Page 4

OIL CONTROL

GLP145	1	Oil Pump Angled	1300
GLP118	1	Oil Pump Straight	1500
GFE119	1	Oil Filter	1300/1500
TT1226	1	Rocker Assy. Oil Feed Kit	1300/1500
TT1365	1	Basic Oil Cooler Installation Kit	1300/1500
ARO9807	1	Oil Cooler Radiator (10 Row)	1300
ARA221	1	Oil Cooler Radiator (13 Row)	1500

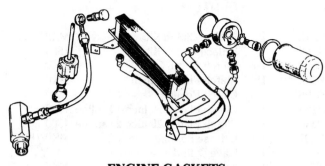

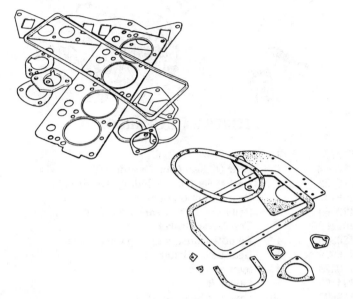

ENGINE GASKETS

AJM1149	1	Decoke Set (Up To Engine No. FH25000)	1300
AJM1209	1	Decoke Set (Engine No. FH25001 On)	1300
AJM1195	1	Decoke Set (Engine No. FH28001 On)	1500
AJM279	1	Conversion Gasket Set	1300/1500
AJM374	1	Head Gasket Flat Topped Block	1300
AJM373	1	Head Gasket Recessed Block	1300/1500
AJM414	1	Rocker Cover Gasket	1300/1500
AJM517	1	Sump Gasket	1300/1500
AJM648	1	Manifold to Head Gasket (also used when fitting FS1400 or TT1400 manifolds to 1500 model)	1300
AJM681	1	Manifold to Head Gasket	1500
GEG701	1	Exhaust Pipe Gasket	1300
GEG739	1	Exhaust Pipe Gasket	1500
GZC1400	1	Oil Filler Cap	1300/1500
22G2115	1	Sump Drain Plug	1300/1500

EXHAUST

GEX1439	1	Front Pipe	MKIV
GEX1620	1	Front Pipe	1500
GEX1621	1	Intermediate Pipe	1500
GEX3668	1	Rear Silencer	MKIV1500
FSSP4	1	2 Piece System, Stainless Steel	MKIV
FSSP5	1	3 Piece System, Stainless Steel	1500
GEG701	1	Front Pipe to Manifold Gasket	MKIV
GEG739	1	Front Pipe to Manifold Gasket	1500
GEX7359	2	Rubber Hanger Strap	MKIV1500
TT1400	1	Extractor Manifold, Tubular	
FS1400	1	As Above, Stainless Steel	
TT5420	1	Twin Oval Box System	
TT5412	1	GT Twin Round Box System	
FS5412	1	Stainless Steel Twin Oval Box System	

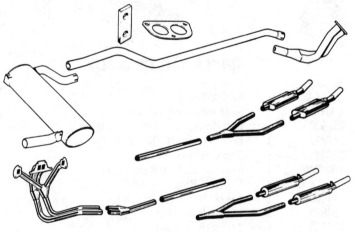

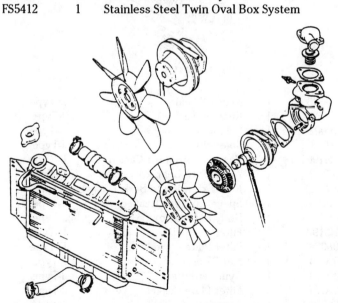

COOLING

GTS102	1	Thermostat (74C-Summer)	MKIV/1500
GTS104	1	Thermostat (82C-Winter)	MKIV/1500
115467	1	Thermostat Gasket	MKIV/1500
GTR108	1	Temperature Sending Unit	MKIV/1500
GRC114	1	Radiator Cap (13Lbs)	MKIV/1500
GCB11088	1	Fan Belt	MKIV/1500
GWP128	1	Water Pump (Bolt on Fan Type)	MKIV/1500
UKC774	1	Water Pump (Fan On Viscous Coupling)	1500
UKC3532	1	Viscous Coupling	1500
UKC759	1	Viscous Coupling Locking Sleeve	1500
138701	1	Water Pump to Housing Gasket	MKIV/1500
402823	1	Radiator New	MKIV/1500
402823R	1	Radiator Exchange	MKIV/1500
GRH533	1	Top Radiator Hose	MKIV/1500
GRH265	1	Bottom Radiator Hose	MKIV/1500

Stockport 061 480 6402.   Shipley 0274 594071.   Darlington 0325 281343.

moss

Page 5

CLUTCH

GCK273	1	3-Piece Clutch Kit	MKIV
GCK160	1	3-Piece Clutch Kit	1500
GCC197	1	Clutch Cover	MKIV
GCP222	1	Clutch Plate 6.5 inch	MKIV
GCC196	1	Clutch Cover	1500
GCP103	1	Clutch Plate 7.25 inch 10 spline	1500
GCP230	1	Clutch Plate 7.25 inch 23 spline	1500
GRB207	1	Release Bearing	MKIV/1500
144716	1	Slave Cylinder, Alloy Body	MKIV
515279	1	Seal Kit for above	MKIV
GSY103	1	Slave Cylinder, Cast Iron Body	1500
GRK4019	1	Seal Kit for above	1500
GMC205	1	Master Cylinder	MKIV/1500
GRK1029	1	Master Cylinder Seal Kit	MKIV/1500
125217	1	Clutch Pedal Boot	MKIV/1500
150881	1	Pedal Rubber	MKIV/1500
114438	1	Pedal Return Spring	MKIV/1500
PJ8808	1	Pedal Clevis Pin	MKIV/1500

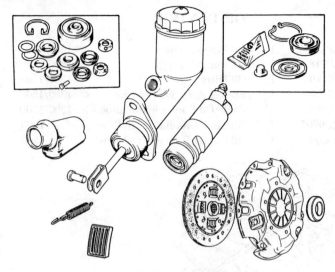

THREE RAIL GEARBOX

519770	1	Gear Lever Bush Kit
88G564	1	Rear Oil Seal (Non Overdrive)
515122	1	Gasket Set (Not Including Overdrive)
106437	1	Rear Extention Gasket
122569	1	Bell Housing to Gearbox Gasket
106269	1	Top Cover Gasket
120305	1	Remote Housing to Top Cover Gasket
706919	1	Gear Lever Gaiter
150328	4	Syncro Ring
144595	1	Layshaft
119893	50	Layshaft Bearing
157732	1	Tailshaft Bearing
104433	2	Mainshaft Bearing (Front and Centre)
106448	1	Reverse Lever Fulcrum Pin

SINGLE RAIL GEARBOX

88G564	1	Rear Oil Seal
22G1420	1	Rear Extention Gasket
157690	1	Bell Housing to Gearbox Gasket
132292	1	Front Oil Seal (When Fitted)
22G1911	1	Top Cover Gasket
TRS912	1	Selector Rail Oil Ring
150328	4	Synchro Ring
144595	1	Layshaft
119893	50	Layshaft Bearing
157732	1	Tailshaft Bearing
104433	2	Mainshaft Bearing (Front and Centre)
DAM1714	1	Reverse Lever Fulcrum Pin
22G2115	1	Filler Plug
155660	1	Drain Plug (Magnetic)

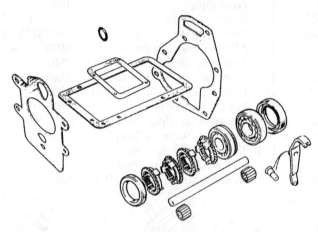

OVERDRIVE

7H8325	1	Rear Oil Seal	D-Type
NKC39A	1	Rear Oil Seal	J-Type
010002	1	Solenoid	D-Type
NKC41	1	Solenoid	J-Type
37H1901	1	Casing to Adaptor Gasket	D-Type
106437	1	Adaptor to Gearbox Gasket	D-Type
NKC87	1	Rear Extension to Body Gasket	J-Type
NKC86	1	Spacer to Body Gasket	J-Type
37H1901	1	Body to Gearbox Gasket	J-Type
7H8197	1	Filter	D-Type
506098	1	Filter Plate Gasket	D-Type
NKC53	1	Flat Filter	J-Type
NKC23	1	Cylinder Filter	J-Type
NKC76	1	Filter Plate Gasket	J-Type
520999A	1	Overdrive Switch	MKIV/1500

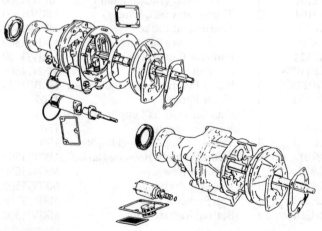

Spitfire Parts Price List

(Prices effective as of 1st July 1991)
PLEASE NOTE THAT ALL PRICES EXCLUDE VAT

Part No.	Price	DCDE	Part No.	Price	DCDE	Part No.	Price	DCDE	Part No.	Price	DCDE	Part No.	Price	DCDE
010002	55.00	CX	144595	23.50	AA	37H6132	0.30	LL	717601	13.25	MX	915634	35.00	MX
036411	0.45	MX	144716	42.06	MX	402823	119.00	LI	718716	21.00	MX	917248	16.00	TZ
042425	1.65	LH	144962	41.00	AA	402823R	80.00	TI	718717	21.00	MX	917249	16.00	TZ
102488	0.20	LD	144962B	25.00	MX	402823SUR	50.00	GS	722675	13.00	QX	AAU1908A	2.95	SM
102689	3.05	AA	144965	4.00	MX	506098	0.20	AT	724031M	4.00	MX	AAU2850	7.80	LL
104433	10.00	MX	145197	0.95	AA	511842	0.50	TZ	725117	18.00	MX	AAU3635	23.50	LL
104582	1.30	AA	145328	3.62	LW	514191	7.20	KA	725525	2.95	AT	AE20139020	24.00	QP
104749	2.50	MX	145933	3.00	AA	514191B	3.50	MX	727581	6.10	MH	AE20139030	24.00	QP
105131	4.00	MX	146454	13.50	AA	514370	9.60	KA	727591	6.10	MH	AE20139040	24.00	QP
106269	0.30	LD	147279	25.00	TX	514370B	3.25	MX	728631	12.50	CX	AE20139STD	24.00	QP
106437	0.20	LD	150277	9.00	MH	515122	2.00	MX	728641	12.50	CX	AEU2778	24.00	QP
106448	0.30	KA	150328	6.00	MX	515279	0.65	MX	7H8197	9.95	CX	AEW2171005	2.80	QP
106663	0.55	AA	150881	1.20	AA	516227	4.00	LL	7H8325	3.55	MX	AEW2171015	2.80	QP
109023	13.30	RC	150881	1.20	AA	517700	16.50	LL	806634	5.00	MX	AEW2171STD	2.80	QP
109024	13.30	RC	152616	25.00	TX	518313	2.75	MX	806635	5.00	MX	AHA7373	14.50	MX
114438	0.57	AA	152961	9.70	NP	519582	35.00	TX	806638	8.75	MX	AHA7374	14.50	MX
114749	0.25	LD	153886	6.70	CX	519770	9.50	AA	806639	8.75	MX	AHH5839	3.00	AT
115467	0.25	MX	155307	0.83	KA	519988	18.00	MX	806707	10.00	MX	AJM1149	18.40	LD
117578	6.20	RC	155308	1.00	KA	520082	NLA		807030	10.00	MX	AJM1195	21.50	LD
117853	3.90	BH	155310	0.60	MX	520083	4.45	SM	809716	7.00	MX	AJM1209	22.75	LD
117952	4.55	NA	155357	3.50	AA	520341	2.50	TZ	813365	19.75	MX	AJM279	8.40	LD
119450	4.30	KA	155416	25.00	MX	520999A	9.30	SM	813366	19.75	MX	AJM373	5.00	LD
119451	1.60	AA	155430	33.50	SM	533360A	9.60	BH	813745	6.50	MX	AJM374	8.20	LD
119813	2.00	MX	155660	6.00	MX	545254	18.00	CO	813746	6.50	MX	AJM414	1.50	LD
119893	0.35	BH	155751	1.50	MX	545254HC	18.00	TO	813753	6.50	MX	AJM517	2.20	LD
120138	0.60	LL	155753	0.27	AA	569924B	15.00	CX	813754	6.50	MX	AJM648	1.95	LD
120139	1.30	MX	155907030	24.00	QP	576469	6.50	MX	813893	20.00	TZ	AJM681	3.30	LD
120305	0.10	LD	155907040	24.00	QP	577473A	1.75	MH	813894	27.25	AA	ALH1527	0.15	MX
120694	37.25	MC	155907STD	24.00	QP	607201A	2.00	MX	815010	14.00	MX	ARA221	35.00	MC
121766	3.26	BA	155928	55.00	MX	607824	10.00	MX	815279RP	41.50	CX	ARO9807	30.50	MX
122022	0.95	MX	156024	8.00	MH	610675	7.50	MX	815391	145.00	AC	AUD580E	NYA	TI
122324A	0.40	MX	156044	18.00	CX	612792	8.50	MX	815392	133.00	AC	AUD580ES	50.00	GS
122569	0.20	LD	156137	5.50	QX	612806	5.00	MX	818871	21.50	CX	AUD624E	NYA	TI
125074	1.00	CX	156342	4.95	QX	612962	1.30	MH	818871RP	10.00	MX	AUD624ES	50.00	GS
125217	2.50	MX	156346	4.95	QX	613169	0.27	AA	818872	21.50	CX	AUD665E	110.00	GI
125481A	8.00	MX	157229	1.00	LW	613766	0.20	AA	818872RP	10.00	MX	AUD665ES	100.00	GS
125482	8.00	MX	157476	1.30	MX	613766	0.20	AA	819801	15.00	MX	AUE811A	2.10	SE
128135	50.00	MX	157508	2.95	MX	613886	0.27	AA	819802	15.00	MX	BHA4966	25.00	MX
128356	0.06	AA	157690	0.40	MX	619383	0.37	AH	819803	4.20	MX	BHM7057	4.70	LL
128978	9.70	NA	157732	8.00	MX	620403	3.15	MX	819804	4.20	MX	BP6ES	1.70	MX
12G2125	0.20	LD	158729	1.35	AA	621757	6.00	AH	820715B	15.00	CX	BR0TSP	7.95	CO
131312	0.80	MX	158966	24.75	SM	621811	7.50	QX	822401B	45.00	WX	BR0TSP1	7.95	CO
131796	0.75	MX	159130E	60.00	MI	623843	0.50	MX	822431	25.00	CX	BTB440	9.60	BH
131806	1.25	MX	159130ES	20.00	GS	624193	3.50	MX	822434	NYA		C27290	12.00	MX
132292	2.20	MX	159131E	60.00	MI	624729	0.40	MX	822451	49.50	MX	C8939A	4.00	AA
133568	2.00	MX	159131ES	20.00	GS	624730	12.30	TX	822491	61.50	CX	CAR1	55.00	CX
133915	3.00	MX	159372	6.00	MX	624733	12.30	TX	822501	49.50	TX	CHA615	1.80	MX
134065	12.20	BH	159640B	65.00	MX	625687	3.50	MX	88G329	6.25	MB	CHM228	1.80	MX
134529	6.60	QX	159656	26.00	AA	626859	13.70	AH	88G564	2.50	NA	CLZ410	0.35	AA
136487	1.50	CX	159701	9.00	MII	627190	5.50	MX	88G606	14.00	MX	CSA6011	110.00	CX
136869	4.00	MX	18G8642	4.09	LC	629584	7.50	MX	88G607	14.00	MX	CUD1041	6.00	SE
138316	5.00	MX	18G9004	3.25	MX	706422	2.80	MX	903097	31.00	AA	CZA3310	7.50	MA
138701	0.30	LD	201246	25.00	MX	706423	2.80	MX	903097RP	12.00	MX	CZA3311	7.50	MA
139386	1.08	MC	211126	1.20	LD	706807	13.85	CX	903098	31.00	AA	DAM1714	6.30	AA
13H3471A	6.00	BU	213689	160.00	MX	706919	6.60	AA	903098RP	12.00	MX	DAM5079	5.70	NA
13H6084	7.00	SM	217033	36.50	AA	707349	28.50	CX	908970	32.00	CX	FS1400	109.50	CY
140892	0.66	KA	218959	30.00	SM	707931	30.00	AA	909029	15.00	MX	FS5412	152.00	CH
140919	30.00	MX	22G1420	0.30	LD	710290	10.50	AH	909351	22.00	MX	FSSP4	147.00	CX
140919B	14.00	MX	22G1911	0.75	LD	713036	2.50	MX	909352	22.00	MX	FSSP5	162.00	CX
140920	30.00	MX	22G2115	0.86	AA	713037	2.00	MX	909663	49.50	MX	FZX1122E	125.00	GI
140920B	14.00	MX	27H4146A	15.00	BU	713038	2.00	MX	909664	49.50	MX	FZX1122ES	100.00	GS
141648	0.80	MX	305931	160.00	TX	713501	0.25	AA	909797	22.00	MX	FZX1258E	125.00	GI
142534	5.00	SM	305931R	47.25	MI	713511	0.18	MX	909798	22.00	MX	FZX1258ES	100.00	GS
142597	29.50	MH	305931SUR	100.00	GS	715693	25.75	AA	911101	63.50	AA	GAC4022	25.50	MX
142598	29.50	MH	305932	160.00	TX	715821	2.50	MX	911102	63.50	AA	GAC4089	3.60	MA
143215	1.40	AA	305932R	47.25	MI	715885	10.00	AA	911107	26.00	MX	GAC6050X	2.75	MX
143456	4.00	MX	305932SUR	100.00	GS	715886	10.00	AA	911108	25.00	MX	GAC6051X	2.75	MX
143552	3.00	MX	311594B	27.50	CX	716180	8.00	TZ	911327B	102.10	TX	GAC6052X	1.66	MX
144370	6.50	MX	311595B	27.50	CX	716182B	52.50	CX	915633	35.00	MX	GAC6053X	1.66	MX
144504	0.50	MX	37H1901	0.95	AT	716200	5.00	MX	915633/4	65.00	MX	GAC6054X	1.66	MX

Spitfire Parts Price List

(Prices effective as of 1st July 1991)
PLEASE NOTE THAT ALL PRICES EXCLUDE VAT

Part No.	Price	DCDE	Part No.	Price	DCDE	Part No.	Price	DCDE	Part No.	Price	DCDE
GAC8020X	1.50	QX	GSC104	1.55	JN	NZX4013	5.40	SE	TKC3417	37.00	NN
GAE191A	7.00	SM	GSC118	2.85	VN	PJ8807	0.35	AA	TKC419R	90.00	TI
GBD154	15.00	QX	GSD272	6.50	MX	PJ8808	0.51	AA	TKC419SUR	30.00	GS
GBH166	8.57	LL	GSD273	6.50	MX	PKC1466E	NYA		TKC770E	NYA	
GBH175	8.72	LL	GSD295	7.00	MX	PKC1467E	NYA		TKC940	25.00	CH
GBH216	8.65	LL	GSD410	8.40	LP	QHQSK88	55.00	MX	TKC941	25.00	CH
GBP574	11.07	JA	GSJ155B	8.50	MX	QHQSK88ALH	20.00	MX	TRS912	0.10	NA
GBS749	15.30	JC	GSJ158	8.70	BA	QHQSK88ARH	20.00	MX	TT1226	14.00	CY
GCB11088	2.95	VX	GSJ158B	6.00	MX	RKC1624B	14.00	MX	TT1307	13.00	QY
GCC196	46.50	EF	GSV1104	3.95	MX	RKC3305E	30.00	MI	TT1365	32.00	MY
GCC197	29.75	EF	GSV1105	3.95	MX	RKC3305ES	50.00	GS	TT1400	66.00	MH
GCK160	99.90	EF	GSY103	42.06	LC	RKC362B	27.50	CX	TT4301	16.00	MY
GCK273	79.90	EF	GTR108	5.80	BQ	RKC363B	27.50	CX	TT5412	85.00	MY
GCL111	13.06	VN	GTS102	3.05	ER	RKC5044	84.00	SM	TT5420	65.00	MY
GCP103	22.75	EF	GTS104	3.05	ER	RTC1174	7.50	SM	TT7325	28.50	CY
GCP222	25.75	EF	GUJ101	7.20	BA	RTC1176	7.50	SM	TT7345	32.00	CY
GCP230	34.25	EF	GUJ115	8.00	BA	RTC1177	9.50	SM	TT7346	6.00	MX
GCS1001S	0.26	MX	GWB199	6.00	MX	RTC1753	10.50	MX	TT7403	36.00	CY
GCS105	1.40	JN	GWB611	2.95	ZX	RTC1753010	11.00	MX	TT7404	36.00	CY
GCS118	1.45	JN	GWB811	2.95	ZX	RTC1753020	11.00	MX	TT7430A	18.00	CY
GDC123	2.75	VN	GWC1110	10.38	LL	RTC1753030	11.00	MX	TT7462	146.00	WY
GDC136	3.15	VN	GWC1202	12.93	LL	RTC1753040	15.00	MX	UKC1110	3.00	MX
GEG701	1.35	LD	GWP128	32.50	BX	RTC1754	10.00	MX	UKC1427R	NYA	
GEG739	3.15	LD	GWW111	40.00	TZ	RTC1754010	11.00	MX	UKC1428R	NYA	
GEU2206	64.00	NI	GWW125	12.20	BJ	RTC1754020	11.00	MX	UKC2460	3.50	LW
GEU4405	20.00	NI	GWW202M	0.63	BJ	RTC1754030	11.00	MX	UKC2992	0.45	LD
GEU8206	64.00	NI	GWW802	2.60	MX	RTC1754040	12.00	MX	UKC3532	55.00	MX
GEU9405	20.00	NI	GWW914	5.40	BJ	RTC9819CB	16.00	CO	UKC3918	8.50	TZ
GEX1439	NYA		GWW918	6.00	TX	SBP101	6.75	MX	UKC4805	10.00	MX
GEX1620	36.25	ES	GXE8206	64.00	NI	SBP102	6.75	MX	UKC5334	6.50	MX
GEX1621	14.50	ES	GXE9405	20.00	NI	SBP107	34.50	MX	UKC7274	18.30	SM
GEX3668	70.00	ES	GXE9405ES	10.00	GS	SBP108	34.50	MX	UKC759	1.05	AA
GEX7359	0.30	EB	GZC1400	4.80	BT	SBP109	15.00	MX	UKC774	30.00	MX
GFE1037	7.20	VH	HZX1179E	NYA	TI	SBP110	15.00	MX	UKC8372	8.00	MX
GFE1063	7.50	VH	HZX1179ES	50.00	GS	SBP111	23.00	MX	UKC8523	6.00	AA
GFE119	7.30	VL	JN2107	0.12	AA	SBP112	23.00	MX	WKC1650	145.00	TX
GFS35X	0.22	MX	MGL0083	14.95	CO	SBP113	10.00	MX	WKC2466	120.00	AC
GFU2124	2.45	BG	MGL0216	NYA		SBP114	10.00	MX	WKC2467	120.00	AC
GGE103	7.70	BG	MGL0228	NYA		SBP115	18.50	MX	WKC3414	30.00	MX
GGE104	7.70	BG	MGL6711	6.00	CO	SBP116	18.50	MX	WKC3450	375.00	CX
GHB105	11.10	EQ	MGL6811	5.00	CO	SBP118	41.50	CX	WKC3621PA	52.50	AA
GHB117	9.10	EQ	MGL9800	3.00	GO	SBP119	NLA		WKC3626PA	11.75	CX
GHF1230	0.07	BM	MLW1111-13	59.95	MX	SBP120	NLA		WPS4695	25.50	MX
GHF1532	0.05	BM	MLW1112-13	59.95	MX	SBP121	6.75	MX	WWC466	95.00	WW
GHF1582	0.12	MX	MLW1113-13	59.95	MX	SBP122	6.75	MX	WWP466	54.00	WW
GHK1021	17.60	EQ	MLW1114-13	59.95	MX	SBP133	22.50	MX	WZX1101A	4.00	SE
GHK1029	15.10	EQ	MLW1115-13	63.25	MX	SBP134	22.50	MX	WZX1300	4.00	SE
GHS111	1.05	EU	MLW1116-13	63.25	MX	SBP137	27.25	CX	WZX1442	9.20	SE
GHT152	8.30	VF	MLW1117B20	19.50	MX	SBP138	27.25	CX	WZX1443	7.70	SE
GLP118	42.00	MX	MLW1117B45	19.50	MX	SBP139	27.95	CX	XKC1781B	110.00	CX
GLP145	44.00	MX	NKC23	12.80	AT	SBP140	27.95	CX	XKC2887PA	44.00	CX
GMC205	52.48	LL	NKC39A	5.00	AT	SBP141B	45.75	WY	XKC2888PA	22.55	CX
GMC220	62.75	LL	NKC41	100.00	AT	SBP142B	45.75	WY	XKC2916PA	11.75	CX
GMC224	65.00	MX	NKC53	6.00	CX	SBP143	10.25	MX	XKC2917PA	11.00	MX
GMC226	136.85	LL	NKC76	1.00	MX	SBP144	19.50	MX	YKC1431	8.50	MX
GRA110	1.10	JN	NKC86	1.45	LD	SBP152	9.95	CX	YKC1454	4.00	MX
GRA114	1.30	JN	NKC87	1.45	LD	SBP153	9.95	CX	YKC1455	4.00	MX
GRB207	17.10	BV	NSK4040PA	38.00	CX	SBP154	13.80	CX	YKC1456	4.00	MX
GRC114	3.05	EX	NSK4041PA	38.00	CX	SBP155	4.85	CX	YKC1457	4.00	MX
GRH265	6.48	EE	NSK4140PA	37.60	CX	SBP156	4.85	CX	YKC2837	35.00	MX
GRH533	4.25	EE	NSK4141PA	37.60	CX	SBP157	8.25	CX	YKC2838	35.00	MX
GRK1029	4.08	LC	NSK4240PA	25.50	CX	SBP158	8.25	CX	ZKC2099	0.60	CX
GRK2010	4.09	LC	NSK4241PA	25.50	CX	TKC1155XR	95.00	WI	ZKC3442	9.50	MX
GRK4019	3.50	LC	NSK4500PA	3.20	CX	TKC1155XSUR	20.00	GS	ZKC751	0.60	QX
GRK5005	7.50	LC	NSK4540PA	94.00	CY	TKC1408E	NYA				
GSA267	15.00	MX	NSK4541PA	94.00	CX	TKC1884	17.00	CX			
GSA385	13.95	MX	NSK4542PA	94.00	CX	TKC2053	22.00	MX			

MGL6411

DRIVE TRAIN

TKC770E	1	Propshaft Assy. (Strap Type)	MKIV
TKC1408E	1	Propshaft Assy. O/D (Strap Type)	MKIV
143215	8	Propshaft Straps	MKIV
PKC1466E	1	Propshaft Assy. (CV-Joint Type)	1500
PKC1467E	1	Propshaft Assy. O/D (CV-Joint Type)	1500
GUJ101	3/4	Universal Joint (Sealed Type)	MKIV/1500
GUJ115	3/4	Universal Joint (Greaseable)	MKIV/1500
128135	2	Rear Halfshaft (Narrow Track) (Up To Ch. No. FH50000)	MKIV
155928	2	Rear Halfshaft (Wide Track) (Ch. No. FH50001 On)	MKIV/1500
GHB117	2	Rear Hub Bearing Outer	MKIV/1500
GHS111	2	Rear Hub Seal Outer	MKIV/1500
117853	2	Rear Hub Bearing Inner	MKIV/1500
128978	2	Rear Hub Seal Inner	MKIV/1500
GHK1029	2	Rear Hub Bearing Kit	MKIV/1500

'E' suffix on above part numbers indicates that unit is available as an exchange item.

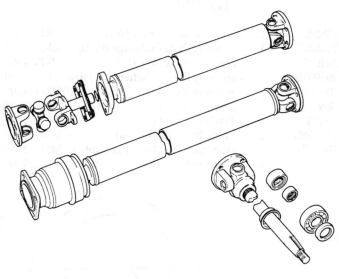

FUEL SYSTEMS

AUD580E	1	Exchange Carbs. (Pair) (Eng. No. FH1 - 59688)	1300
AUD624E	1	Exchange Carbs. (Pair) (Eng. No. FH59689 - 75000)	1300
AUD665E	1	Exchange Carbs. (Pair) (Eng. No. FM28001 - 53446)	1500
FZX1258E	1	Exchange Carbs. (Pair) (Eng. No. FM53447 - 105277)	1500
FZX1122E	1	Exchange Carbs. (Pair) (Eng. No. FM105278 - 118373)	1500
HZX1179E	1	Exchange Carbs. (Pair) (Eng. No. FM118374 On)	1500
UKC8372	1	Heat Shield	MKIV/1500
UKC2992	4	Gasket, Carb. to Manifold	MKIV/1500
12G2125	2	Gasket, Carb. to Air Cleaner	MKIV/1500
WZX1101A	2	Float Bowl Valve Kit	MKIV/1500
WZX1300	2	Float Replacement Kit	MKIV/1500
AUE811A	1	Gasket Pack	MKIV/1500
CUD1041	2	ABT Needle (FZX1258 Carb.)	1500
NZX4013	2	ADN Needle (FZX1122/HZX1179)	1500
WZX1442	1	Service Kit w/Jets (Eng. No. FM28001 - 105277)	1500
WZX1443	1	Service Kit w/Jets (Eng. No. FM105278 On)	1500
TKC2053	1	Tank Sender Unit	MKIV/1500
RKC1624B	1	Fuel Pump, Repro. Item (Eng. No. FM28000 - 93156)	1500
TKC3417	1	Fuel Pump, Original Equipment (Eng. No. FH1 - 74999;FM93157 On)	MKIV/1500
UKC8523	1	Pump Spacer (TKC3417 Only)	MKIV/1500
725117	1	Fuel Filler Cap	MKIV/1500
152961	1	Fuel Filter (USA Type)	MKIV/1500
GFE1037	2	Air Filter	MKIV
GFE1063	2	Air Filter	1500
102488	4	Air Filter Gasket	MKIV/1500
141648	1	Air Filter Seal	MKIV/1500

DIFFERENTIAL

DAM5079	1	Pinion Seal (Front)	MKIV/1500
117952	2	Output Shaft Seal (Side)	MKIV/1500
22G2115	1	Filler Plug	MKIV/1500
114749	1	Casing Gasket	MKIV/1500
BTB440	1	Pinion Bearing (Front) Outer	MKIV/1500
134065	1	Pinion Bearing (Front) Inner	MKIV/1500
145933	1	Pinion Bearing Distance Tube	MKIV/1500
533360A	2	Output Bearing (Side)	MKIV/1500
GHB105	2	Carrier Bearing (Up To Ch. No. FH106101)	MKIV/1500
UKC4805	2	Carrier Bearing (Ch. No. FH106102 On)	1500

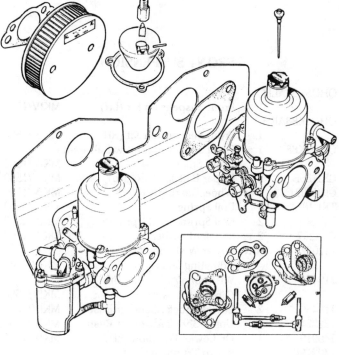

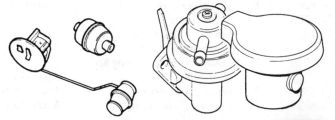

STEERING

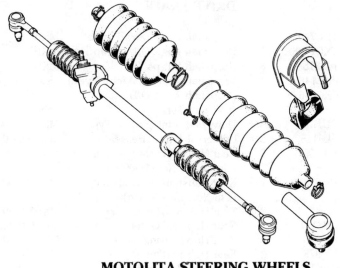

305932	1	Steering Rack New (RHD)	MKIV/1500
305932R	1	Steering Rack Exchange (RHD)	MKIV/1500
305931	1	Steering Rack New (LHD)	MKIV/1500
305931R	1	Steering Rack Exhchange (LHD)	MKIV/1500
GSV1104	1	Steering Rack Boot (Remote End)	MKIV/1500
GSV1105	1	Steering Rack Boot (Pinion End)	MKIV/1500
GSJ158	2	Track Rod End (OE)	MKIV/1500
GSJ158B	2	Track Rod End (Repro)	MKIV/1500
139386	2	Steering Rack Mounting Rubber	MKIV/1500
156024	2	Steering Rack Mounting U-Bolt	MKIV/1500

MOTOLITA STEERING WHEELS

MLW1117B20	1	Centre Boss (Steering Lock Under Column)	MKIV/1500
MLW1117B45	1	Centre Boss (Steering Lock On Side Of Column)	1500
MLW1116-13	1	Dished Wooden Wheel	MKIV/1500
MLW1115-13	1	Flat Wooden Wheel	MKIV/1500
MLW1114-13	1	Black Dished Leather Wheel	MKIV/1500
MLW1112-13	1	Black Flat Leather Wheel	MKIV/1500
MLW1113-13	1	Polished Dished Leather Wheel	MKIV/1500
MLW1111-13	1	Polished Flat Leather Wheel	MKIV/1500

*wheels can be 13, 14 or 15" diameter - listed here are the 13" variants. Add -14 or -15 to part no. to order other sizes.

FRONT SUSPENSION

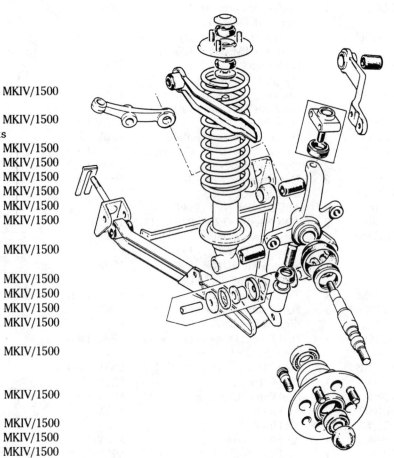

QHQSK88ALH	1	Front Suspension Kit (LH)	MKIV/1500
QHQSK88ARH	1	Front Suspension Kit (RH)	MKIV/1500
QHQSK88	1	Front Suspension Kit w/Ball Joints (Both Sides)	MKIV/1500
GSJ155B	2	Upper Ball Joint (Repro)	MKIV/1500
GHK1021	2	Wheel Bearing Kit	MKIV/1500
TKC1884	2	Coil Spring	MKIV/1500
TT4301	2	Coil Spring Road Uprated	MKIV/1500
GSA267	2	Shock Absorber	MKIV/1500
122022	A/R	Lower Wishbone Arm Adjusting Shims	MKIV/1500
119451	8	Wishbone Arm Inner Bush (Upper & Lower)	MKIV/1500
119450	2	Lower Shock Absorber Bush	MKIV/1500
122324A	4	Upper Shock Absorber Bush	MKIV/1500
140919	1	OE Lower Trunnion (RH)	MKIV/1500
140919B	1	Repro Trunnion (RH)	
140920	1	OE Lower Trunnion (LH)	MKIV/1500
140920B	1	Repro Trunnion (LH)	
514191	1	Lower Trunnion Fitting Kit (Both Sides)	MKIV/1500
514191B	2	Lower Trunnion Fitting Kit (One Side)	MKIV/1500
102689	2	Wheel Hub Grease Cap	MKIV/1500
140892	4	Bearing (Trunnion)	MKIV/1500

ANTI ROLL BAR

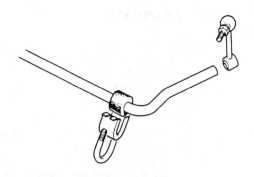

217033	1	Front Anti-roll Bar 7/8"	MKIV/1500
125481A	1	Link Assembly (RH)	MKIV/1500
125482	1	Link Assembly (LH)	MKIV/1500
125074	2	Anti-Roll Bar End Stud	MKIV/1500
155307	2	U-Bolt	MKIV/1500
155308	2	Saddle Clamp	MKIV/1500
155310	2	Mounting Rubber	MKIV/1500

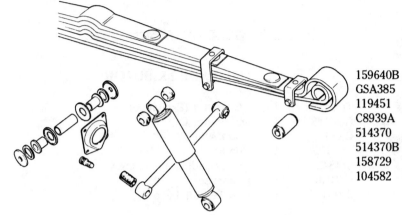

REAR SUSPENSION

159640B	1	Rear Spring Assy.	MKIV/1500
GSA385	2	Rear Shock Absorber	MKIV/1500
119451	4	Radius Rod Bush	MKIV/1500
C8939A	2	Spring Eye Bush	MKIV/1500
514370	1	Lr Trunnion Bush Kit (Car Set)	MKIV/1500
514370B	2	Lr Trunnion Bush Kit (One Side)	MKIV/1500
158729	8	Wheel Stud	MKIV/1500
104582	2	Axle Shaft Oil Deflector Cup	MKIV/1500

BRAKES

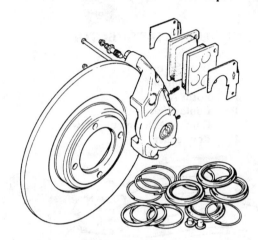

159131E	1	Caliper Assy. Exchange (LH)	MKIV/1500
159130E	1	Caliper Assy. Exchange (RH)	MKIV/1500
GRK5005	1	Caliper Seal Kit	MKIV/1500
GBD154	2	Brake Disc	MKIV1500
GBP574	1	Brake Pad Set	MKIV/1500
BHM7057	1	Brake Pad Fitting Kit	MKIV/1500
201246	2	Brake Drum	MKIV/1500
GWC1202	2	Wheel Cylinder (15mm Bore) (Up To Ch. No. FH80000)	MKIV/1500
18G9004	2	Repair Kit (For GWC1202)	MKIV/1500
GWC1110	2	Wheel Cylinder (18mm Bore) (Ch. No. FH80001 On)	1500
18G8642	2	Repair Kit (For GWC1110)	1500
37H6132	2	Wheel Cylinder Retaining Clip	MKIV/1500
120138	2	Wheel Cylinder Retaining Clip	MKIV/1500
120139	2	Handbrake Lever Boot	MKIV/1500
GBS749	1	Brake Shoe Set	MKIV/1500
GBH216	2	Front Brake Hose	MKIV/1500
GBH175	2	Rear Brake Hose (Narrow Track) (Up To Ch. No. FH50000)	MKIV
GBH166	2	Rear Brake Hose (Wide Track) (Ch. No. FH50001 On)	MKIV/1500
GMC224	1	Brake Master Cylinder, Single System, All Metal Cylinder	
GRK1029	1	Repair Kit for GMC224	
GMC220	1	Brake Master Cylinder Single System Plastic Reservoir	
516227	1	Repair Kit for GMC220	
213689	1	Brake Master Cylinder, Tandem System, Big Cap. (Up To Ch. No. FH80000)	
517700	1	Cylinder Repair Kit For 213689	
GMC226	1	Brake Master Cylinder, Tandem System, Small Cap. (Ch. No. FM80001 On. LHD) (Ch. No. FH130001 On. RHD)	
AAU2850	1	Cylinder Repair Kit For GMC226	
AAU3635	1	Reservoir Seal Kit For GMC226	
125217	1	Master Cylinder Dust Cover	MKIV/1500
150881	1	Brake Pedal Rubber	MKIV/1500
114438	1	Pedal Return Spring	MKIV/1500
PJ8808	1	Pedal Clevis Pin	MKIV/1500
134529	1	Brake Light Switch	MKIV/1500

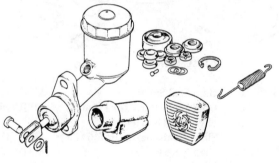

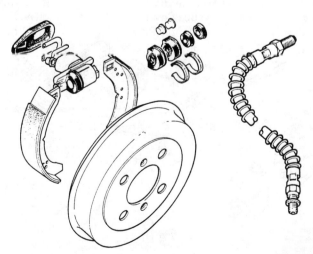

HANDBRAKE

104749	3	Cable End, Forked	MKIV/1500
133915	1	Rear Cable (Narrow Track) (Up To Ch. No. FH50000)	MKIV
159372	1	Rear Cable (Wide Track) (Ch. No. FH50001 On)	MKIV/1500
121766	1	Front Cable	MKIV/1500
JN2107	1	Jam Nut (On Front Cable)	MKIV/1500
CLZ410	3	Clevis Pin (At End Forks)	MKIV/1500
131806	2	Return Spring (At Wheels)	MKIV/1500
PJ8807	1	Clevis Pin (Front to Rear Cables)	MKIV/1500
131312	1	Handle Grip (Round Type)	MKIV
UKC3918	1	Handle Grip (Shaped Type)	1500

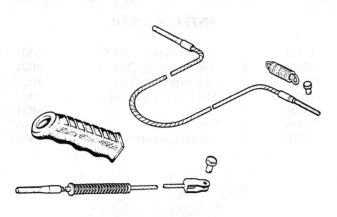

DELCO DISTRIBUTOR

TKC419R	1	Distributor (Exchange)	
GDC123	1	Distributor Cap	
GRA110	1	Rotor Arm	
GCS105	1	Contact Set	
511842	1	Contact Adjustment Screw	
GSC104	1	Condenser	
520341	1	Low Tension Lead	

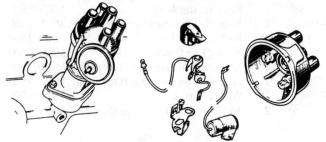

LUCAS DISTRIBUTOR

RKC5044	1	Distributor
GDC136	1	Distributor Cap
GRA114	1	Rotor Arm
GCS118	1	Contact Set
GCS1001S	1	Contact Adjustment Screw
GSC118	1	Condenser

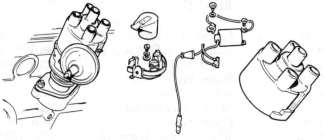

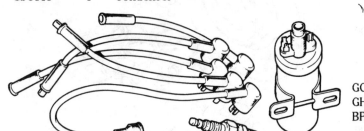

ALL DISTRIBUTORS

GCL111	1	Ignition Coil	MKIV/1500
GHT152	1	High Tension Lead Set	MKIV/1500
BP6ES	4	Spark Plugs (NGK)	MKIV/1500

ELECTRICS

GEU4405	1	Gold Seal Starter	MKIV/1500
GEU2206	1	Gold Seal Alternator (16ACR)	MKIV/1500
GEU9405	1	Silver Seal Starter	MKIV/1500
GEU8206	1	Silver Seal Alternator (16ACR)	MKIV/1500
GGE103	1	High Note Horn	MKIV/1500
GGE104	1	Low Note Horn	MKIV/1500
607201A	1	Fuse Box Cover	MKIV/1500
GFS35X	A/R	Fuse 35 Amp Blow	MKIV/1500

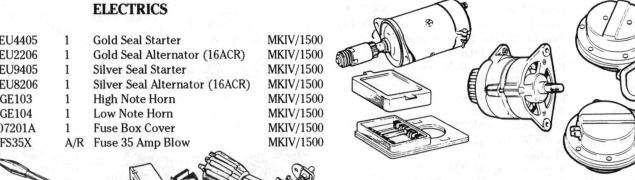

SWITCHES

158966	1	Indicator Switch	MKIV/1500
156044	1	Hazard Switch	MKIV/1500
AAU1908A	1	Courtesy Lamp Switch	MKIV/1500
13H6084	1	Reverse Light Switch	MKIV/1500
218959	1	Ignition Switch	1500
GFU2124	1	Flasher unit (2 Pin)	MKIV/1500
150277	1	Horn Push ('Shield' Logo)	MKIV
159761	1	Horn Push ('TRIUMPH' Logo)	MKIV/1500
142534	1	Horn Brush	MKIV/1500
613766	1	Horn Clip	MKIV/1500
1526161	1	Main Lighting Switch	MKIV/1500

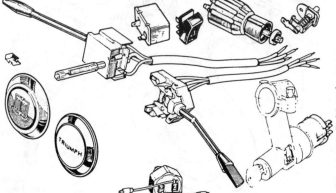

moss

London 081 948 6666.   Birmingham 021 544 5555.   Bristol 0272 232523.

Page 10

LIGHTING

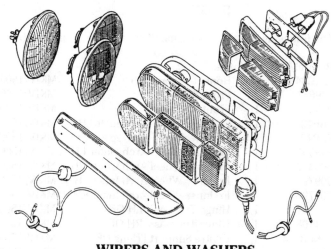

13H3471A	1	Headlamp (RHD)	MKIV/1500
27H4146A	1	Headlamp (LHD)	MKIV/1500
GAC4022	1	Halogen Conversion Kit (RHD)	MKIV/1500
WPS4695	1	Halogen Conversion Kit (LHD)	MKIV/1500
155416	2	Side Indicator Lamp	MKIV/1500
520082	2	Side Indicator Lamp Lens Amber	MKIV/1500
520083	2	Side Indicator Lamp Lens Clear	MKIV/1500
TKC940	1	Rear Lamp Assembly (LH)	MKIV/1500
TKC941	1	Rear Lamp Assembly (RH)	MKIV/1500
RTC1174	2	Reverse Lens Clear	MKIV/1500
RTC1176	2	Rear Indicator Lens Amber	MKIV/1500
RTC1177	2	Stop Lens Red	MKIV/1500
519582	1	Number Plate Lamp Cover (Up To Ch. No. FH116000)	MKIV/1500
UKC7274	2	Number Plate Lamp (Ch. No. FH116001 On)	1500

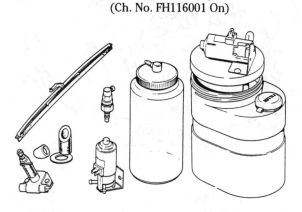

CONTROL CABLES

156342	1	Accelerator Cable (RHD)	MKIV/1500
145197	2	Accelerator Return Spring	MKIV/1500
156346	1	Accelerator Cable (LHD)	TwinCarb
156137	1	Choke Cable (RHD)	MKIV/1500
518313	1	Choke Cable (LHD)	MKIV/1500
624193	1	Fresh Air Vent Control Cable	MKIV/1500
625687	1	Heater Valve Control Cable	MKIV/1500
GSD272	1	Speedo Cable (Non-O/D RHD)	MKIV
GSD273	1	Speedo Cable (O/D)	MKIV/1500
GSD295	1	Speedo Cable (Non-O/D RHD)	1500
GSD410	1	Speedo Cable (Non-O/D LHD)	1500
120694	1	Angle Drive (O/D Only)	MKIV/1500
144370	1	Rev. Counter Cable (RHD)	MKIV
138316	1	Rev. Counter Cable (LHD)	MKIV

WIPERS AND WASHERS

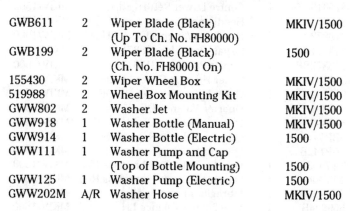

GWB611	2	Wiper Blade (Black) (Up To Ch. No. FH80000)	MKIV/1500
GWB199	2	Wiper Blade (Black) (Ch. No. FH80001 On)	1500
155430	2	Wiper Wheel Box	MKIV/1500
519988	2	Wheel Box Mounting Kit	MKIV/1500
GWW802	2	Washer Jet	MKIV/1500
GWW918	1	Washer Bottle (Manual)	MKIV/1500
GWW914	1	Washer Bottle (Electric)	1500
GWW111	1	Washer Pump and Cap (Top of Bottle Mounting)	1500
GWW125	1	Washer Pump (Electric)	1500
GWW202M	A/R	Washer Hose	MKIV/1500

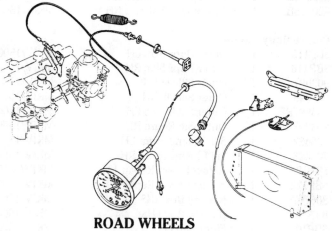

ROAD WHEELS

WWC466	5	Chrome Wire Wheel	MKIV/1500
WWP466	5	Painted Wire Wheel	MKIV/1500
142598	2	Wire Wheel Hub Adaptor (LH)	MKIV/1500
142597	2	Wire Wheel Hub Adaptor (RH)	MKIV/1500
144504	16	Hub Adaptor Nuts	MKIV/1500
AHA7374	2	2-Eared Spinner Knock-Off (LH)	MKIV/1500
AHA7373	2	2-Eared Spinner Knock-Off (RH)	MKIV/1500
88G607	2	Octagonal Spinner (LH)	MKIV/1500
88G606	2	Octagonal Spinner (RH)	MKIV/1500
AHH5839	1	Spanner For Octagonal Spinner	MKIV/1500
88G329	1	Knock-Off Hammer (Lead)	MKIV/1500
C27290	1	Knock-Off Hammer (Copper/Hide)	MKIV/1500
GAC4089	1	Wire Wheel Cleaning Brush	MKIV/1500
155751	16	Steel Wheel Chrome Nut (Stepped)	MKIV/1500
155753	16	Hub Cap Locking Ring (Plastic)	MKIV/1500
716180	4	Hub Cap	MKIV/1500

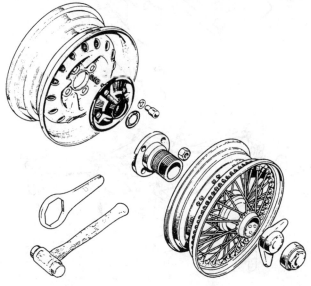

Stockport 061 480 6402.   Shipley 0274 594071.   Darlington 0325 281343.

moss

Page 11

BODY

The following panels are original BL if available, indicated by 'OE' in the description. Otherwise reproduction.

Bonnet/Front Valance

WKC3450	1	Bonnet Assembly, OE	MKIV/1500
909663	1	Front Wing LH	MKIV/1500
909664	1	Front Wing RH	MKIV/1500
SBP133	1	Fr. Wheel Arch Lip Repair LH	MKIV/1500
SBP134	1	Fr. Wheel Arch Lip Repair RH	MKIV/1500
909351	1	Fr. Inner Wheel Arch Outer LH	MKIV/1500
909352	1	Fr. Inner Wheel Arch Outer RH	MKIV/1500
909797	1	Fr. Inner Wheel Arch Inner LH	MKIV/1500
909798	1	Fr. Inner Wheel Arch Inner RH	MKIV/1500
911107	1	Hinge Tube Ass. LH OE	MKIV/1500
911108	1	Hinge Tube Ass. RH OE	MKIV/1500
WKC3414	1	Centre Support Frame OE	MKIV/1500
SBP154	1	BonnetSupport Stay	MKIV/1500
815010	1	Centre Lower Return Edge	MKIV/1500
818871	1	Headlamp/Support Ass. LH OE	MKIV/1500
818872	1	Headlamp/Support Ass. RH OE	MKIV/1500
818871RP	1	Repair Panel for 818871	MKIV/1500
818872RP	1	Repair Panel for 818872	MKIV/1500
911101	1	Outer H/Lamp Cover LH OE	MKIV/1500
911102	1	Outer H/Lamp Cover RH OE	MKIV/1500
815391	1	Quarter Valance OE LH	MKIV/1500
815392	1	Quarter Valance OE RH	MKIV/1500
SBP141B	1	Quarter Valance Repro LH	MKIV/1500
SBP142B	1	Quarter Valance Repro RH	MKIV/1500
TT7403	1	Quarter Valance Fibreglass LH	MKIV/1500
TT7404	1	Quarter Valance Fibreglass RH	MKIV/1500
TT7430A	1	Fibreglass Front Spoiler	MKIV/1500
569924B	1	Side Splash Valance LH	MKIV/1500
820715B	1	Side Splash Valance RH	MKIV/1500

Centre Body/Floors

SBP115	1	Outer Door Skin LH	MKIV/1500
SBP116	1	Outer Door Skin RH	MKIV/1500
903097	1	Outer Sill OE LH	MKIV/1500
903098	1	Outer Sill OE RH	MKIV/1500
903097RP	1	Outer Sill Repro LH	MKIV/1500
903098RP	1	Outer Sill Repro RH	MKIV/1500
706422	1	Sill Closing Front LH	MKIV/1500
706423	1	Sill Closing Front RH	MKIV/1500
SBP121	1	A Post Lower Repair LH	MKIV/1500
SBP122	1	A Post Lower Repair RH	MKIV/1500
806707	1	Battery Box RHS	MKIV/1500
807030	1	Battery Box LHS	MKIV/1500
SBP107	1	Floor Pan LH	MKIV/1500
SBP108	1	Floor Pan RH	MKIV/1500
SBP109	1	Front Repair Section LH	MKIV/1500
SBP110	1	Front Repair Section RH	MKIV/1500
SBP111	1	Rear Repair Section LH	MKIV/1500
SBP112	1	Rear Repair Section RH	MKIV/1500
SBP143	2	Cross Member	MKIV/1500
707349	1	Fibreboard Gearbox Cover	MKIV/1500
TT7325	1	Glassfibre Gearbox Cover	MKIV/1500
806638	1	Inner Sill LH	MKIV/1500
806639	1	Inner Sill RH	MKIV/1500
806634	1	Inner Sill Strengthener LH	MKIV/1500
806635	1	Inner Sill Strengthener RH	MKIV/1500

Chassis Spares

SBP144	1	Repro Front Chassis Member	MKIV/1500
311595B	1	Front Under-Rider Support LH	MKIV/1500
311594B	1	Front Under-Rider Support RH	MKIV/1500
128356	A/R	Shim, Caster Adjustment	MKIV/1500
122022	A/R	Shim, Camber Adjustment	MKIV/1500

BODY, CONTINUED

Rear Body/Boot Compartment

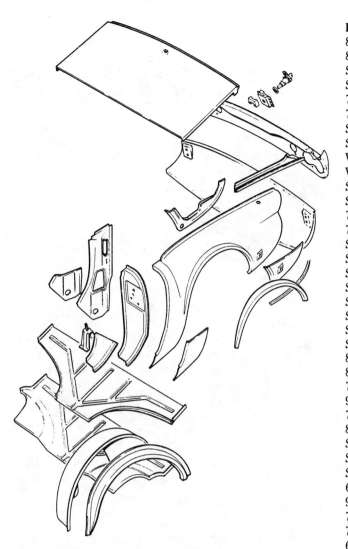

813365	1	B Post, Replica Ass. LH	MKIV/1500
813366	1	B Post, Replica Ass. RH	MKIV/1500
SBP152	1	Lower Repair Panel for 813365	MKIV/1500
SBP153	1	Lower Repair Panel for 813366	MKIV/1500
715885	1	B Post Support Panel LH	MKIV/1500
715886	1	B Post Support Panel RH	MKIV/1500
SBP155	1	Inner B Post Repair Panel LH	MKIV/1500
SBP156	1	Inner B Post Repair Panel RH	MKIV/1500
WKC2466	1	Rear Wing LH	MKIV/1500
WKC2467	1	Rear Wing RH	MKIV/1500
SBP157	1	Inner Rear Wing Repair LH	MKIV/1500
SBP158	1	Inner Rear Wing Repair RH	MKIV/1500
718716	1	Inner Wheel Arch Panel LH	MKIV/1500
718717	1	Inner Wheel Arch Panel RH	MKIV/1500
SBP139	1	Outer Wheel Arch Repair LH	MKIV/1500
SBP140	1	Outer Wheel Arch Repair RH	MKIV/1500
SBP137	1	Rr. Wheel Arch Lip Repair LH	MKIV/1500
SBP138	1	Rr. Wheel Arch Lip Repair RH	MKIV/1500
SBP101	1	Sill Extension Repair LH	MKIV/1500
SPB102	1	Sill Extension Repair RH	MKIV/1500
SBP113	1	Rear Repair Section LH	MKIV/1500
SBP114	1	Rear Repair Section RH	MKIV/1500
813893	1	Rear Drain Channel LH	MKIV/1500
813894	1	Rear Drain Channel RH	MKIV/1500
715821	2	Rear Lower Edge Trim	MKIV/1500
908970	1	Rear Lower Valance	MKIV/1500
716182B	1	Rear Light Panel	MKIV/1500
815279RP	1	Boot Floor Panel	MKIV/1500
SBP118	1	Boot Floor Centre Repair Panel	MKIV/1500
SBP119	1	Boot Floor Corner Repair LH	MKIV/1500
SBP120	1	Boot Floor Corner Repair RH	MKIV/1500
627196	1	Spare Wheel Mounting Bracket	MKIV/1500
911327B	1	Boot Lid	MKIV/1500
710290	1	Boot Lock Mechanism	MKIV/1500
722675	1	Boot LockHandleAssembly	MKIV/1500
624729	1	Boot Lock Handle Gasket	MKIV/1500
619383	1	Boot Catch Striker Block	MKIV/1500

DOOR FITTINGS

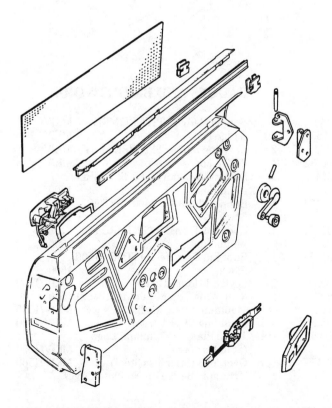

612792	2	Door Glass Outer Seal	MKIV/1500
613169	14	Outer Seal Clip	MKIV/1500
612806	2	Door Glass Inner Seal	MKIV/1500
GHF1582	10	Inner Seal Clip	MKIV/1500
915633	1	Exterior Handle Chrome LH	MKIV/1500
915634	1	Exterior Handle Chrome RH	MKIV/1500
915633/4	1	Exterior Handle Chrome (Pair) (Up To Ch. No. FH100020)	MKIV/1500
YKC2837	1	Ext. Handle Black/Chrome LH	1500
YKC2838	1	Ext. Handle Black/Chrome RH (Ch. No. FH100021 On)	1500
577473A	2	Exterior Handle Gasket	MKIV/1500
819801	1	Interior Handle LH	MKIV/1500
819802	1	Interior Handle RH	MKIV/1500
819803	1	Interior Handle Bezel LH	MKIV/1500
819804	1	Interior Handle Bezel RH	MKIV/1500
621811	2	Winder Handle	MKIV/1500
623843	2	Winder Handle Escutcheon	MKIV/1500
ALH1527	2	Winder Handle Pin	MKIV/1500
CZA3311	1	B-Post Striker Plate LH	MKIV/1500
CZA3310	1	B-Post Striker Plate RH	MKIV/1500
607824	4	Door Hinge	MKIV/1500
CHM228	2	Sound Deadening Mat	MKIV/1500
576469	2	Door Lock	MKIV/1500

INTERIOR TRIM

Part No	Qty	Description	Model
CSA6611	1	Moulded Carpet Set. Black (as original with protective backing)	MKIV/1500
CAR1	1	Carpet Set Black (Standard)	MKIV/1500
NSK4540PA	1	Seat Cover Kit (Non-Reclining)	MKIV
NSK4541PA	1	Seat Cover Kit (Reclining, Leathercloth) (Up To Ch. No. FH100020)	MKIV/1500
NSK4542PA	1	Seat Cover Kit (Reclining Houndstooth) (Ch. No. FH100021 On)	1500
NSK4040PA	1	Door Panel Set (Pair) (Up To Ch. No. FH113678)	MKIV/1500
NSK4041PA	1	Door Panel Set (Pair) (Ch. No. FH113679 On)	1500
GHF1230	22	Trim Clips	MKIV/1500
707931	2	Door Seal OE (Cut to Length)	MKIV/1500
724031M	A/R	Door Seal Repro (2.5M Per Door)	MKIV/1500
727581	1	Door Waist Rail Cover (LH)	MKIV/1500
727591	1	Door Waist Rail Cover (RH)	MKIV/1500
NSK4140PA	1	Rear Quarter Trim Kit (Pair) (Stag Grain, Up To Ch. No. FH113678)	MKIV/1500
NSK4141PA	1	Rear Quarter Trim Kit (Pair) (Longhorn Grain, Ch. No. FH113679 On)	1500
NSK4240PA	1	Rear Cockpit Board (Stag Grain, Up To Ch. No. FH113678)	MKIV/1500
NSK4241PA	1	Rear Cockpit Board (Longhorn Grain, Ch. No. FH113679 On)	1500
WKC3626PA	1	Tunnel Cover Front	1500 *
XKC2916PA	1	Tunnel Cover Side (LH)	1500 *
XKC2917PA	1	Tunnel Cover Side (RH)	1500 *
XKC2887PA	1	Armrest Complete	1500 *
XKC2888PA	1	Armrest (Cover Material Only)	1500 *
813753	1	Glovebox (LH for RHD)	MKIV/1500
813745	1	Glovebox (RH for RHD)	MKIV/1500
813754	1	Glovebox (LH for LHD)	MKIV/1500
813746	1	Glovebox (RH for LHD)	MKIV/1500
728631	1	Glovebox Support (LH)	MKIV/1500
728641	1	Glovebox Support (RH)	MKIV/1500
WKC3621PA	1	Radio Support Frame (Ch. No. FH113679 On)	1500 *
NSK4500PA	1	Radio Support Frame (Cover Material Only) (Ch. No. FH113679 On)	1500 *
YKC1431	1	Boot Trim Board	MKIV/1500
809716	1	Boot Floor Mat	MKIV/1500
706807	1	Spare Wheel Board (Disc Wheel)	MKIV/1500
717601	1	Spare Wheel Cover Material	MKIV/1500

*can be fitted to MKIV

Part Nos suffixed PA indicate Black. Beige can be obtained by substituting AA.

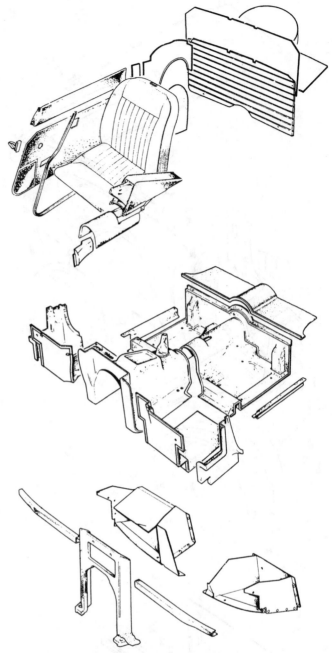

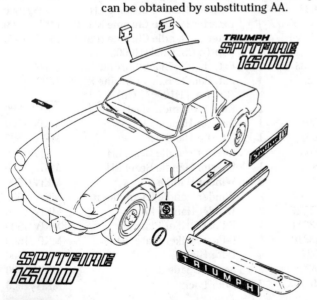

BADGES AND BRIGHTWORK

Part No	Qty	Description	Model
624730	1	Bonnet Badge 'SPITFIRE MKIV'	MKIV
GHF1532	2	Badge Fix	MKIV
624733	2	Rr. Wing Badge 'SPITFIRE MKIV'	MKIV
GHF1532	4	Badge Fix	MKIV
YKC1455	1	Bonnet Transfer '1500 SPITFIRE' Aluminium	1500
YKC1454	1	Bonnet Transfer '1500 SPITFIRE' Black	1500
YKC1457	1	Boot Lid Transfer 'SPITFIRE 1500' Aluminium	1500
YKC1456	1	Boot Lid Transfer 'SPITFIRE 1500' Black	1500
725525	2	Leyland House Badge	MKIV/1500
715693	2	Rear Wing Top Moulding (Black)	1500
613766	18	Moulding Clips Small	MKIV/1500
613886	4	Moulding Clips Large	MKIV/1500
TT7346	1pr.	Tread Plates w/Triumph Logo (Stainless Steel)	MKIV/1500
TT7345	1pr.	Over Sills (Stainless Steel)	MKIV/1500
626859	1	'Triumph' Badge on No Plate Cover	

London 081 948 6666.   Birmingham 021 544 5555.   Bristol 0272 232523.

Page 14

BODY RUBBER

716200	2	Quarter Valance to Bonnet Seal	MKIV/1500
610675	1	Rear Bonnet Seal	MKIV/1500
909029	1	Windscreen Surround Seal	MKIV/1500
917248	1	Windscreen Seal Beading (LH)	MKIV/1500
917249	1	Windscreen Seal Beading (RH)	MKIV/1500
ZKC2099	2	Windscreen Beading Clip	MKIV/1500
ZKC3442	1	Boot Lid Seal	MKIV/1500
620403	2	Windscreen Post Seal	MKIV/1500
612962	2	Bonnet Locating Cone (Rubber)	MKIV/1500
613666	2	Front Arch Seal (Rear)	MKIV/1500

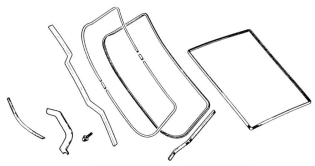

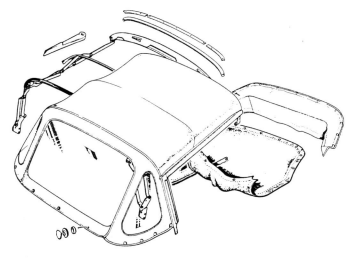

BOOKS

RTC9819CB	Parts Manual
545254	MKIV Workshop Manual (Soft Cover)
545254HC	MKIV Workshop Manual (Hard Cover)
BR0TSP1	Triumph Spitfire Coll.No.1 62-82 Brooklands
BR0TSP	Triumph Spitfire 1962-80
MGL0083	Triumph Spitfire & GT6 Graham Robson
MGL0228	Practical Classics Spitfire Restoration
MGL0216	Spitfire, GT6, Herald, Vitesse Guide to Purchase & Restoration
MGL6711	Spit. MKIV Competition Preparation Manual
MGL6811	Spit. 1500 Competition Preparation Manual
MGL9800	Triumph Tune Catalogue

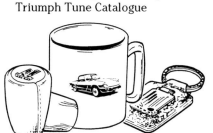

WEATHER EQUIPMENT

XKC1781B	1	Hood Black	MKIV/1500
TT7462	1	Hood (Double Duck) Black	MKIV/1500
WKC1650	1	Hood Frame	MKIV/1500
621757	2	Hood Frame Handle	MKIV/1500
822451	1	Tonneau (RHD) w/o Headrest	MKIV/1500
822491	1	Tonneau (RHD) w/Headrest	MKIV/1500
822501	1	Tonneau (LHD) w/Headrest	MKIV/1500
822401B	1	Hood Cover, Black	MKIV/1500
822431	1	Hood Cover, Black (In Hardtop)	MKIV/1500
822434	1	Hood Cover, Beige (In Hardtop)	MKIV/1500
629584	1	Frame to Windscreen Seal	MKIV/1500
713038	1	Seal Retainer (RH)	MKIV/1500
713036	1	Seal Retainer (Centre)	MKIV/1500
713037	1	Seal Retainer (LH)	MKIV/1500
713511	A/R	Plastic Body Snaps	MKIV/1500
713501	A/R	Snap Socket	MKIV/1500
ZKC751	A/R	Black Enamel Snap Button	MKIV/1500

All Weather Equipment Is Supplied In Black Material Only

ACCESSORIES

GAC6050X	Wooden Gear Knob
GAC6051X	Leather Gear Knob
GAC6052X	Spitfire Key Fob
GAC6053X	Triumph Key Fob (Blue and White)
GAC6054X	Triumph Key Fob (Red and White)
GAC8020X	Spitfire Coffee Mug

SPITFIRE CHASSIS / ENGINE NOS.

MODEL YEAR	CHASSIS NUMBERS[3]		ENGINE NUMBERS	
	UK START	USA START	UK START	USA START
1971	FH1	FK1	FH1E[1]	FK1UE
1972	FH25001	FK25001	FH25001E[1]	FK25001UE
1973	FH50001	FM1	FH50001E[1]	FM1UE
1974	FH60001	FM10001	FH60001E[1]	FM10001UE[2]
1975	FH75001	FM28001	FM28001E	FM28001UE[2]
1976	FH80001	FM40001	FM45001E	FM45001UE[2]
1977	FH100020	FM60006	FM85026E	FM85026UE[2]
1978	FH105734	FM70001	FM100735E	FM100735UE[2]
1979	FH130001	FM95001	FM150002E	FM150002UE[2]
1980	FH133501	FM110001	FM168502E	FM168502UE[2]

[1] : LOW COMPRESSION ENGINES ADD 'L' BEFORE 'E' SUFFIX

[1] : HIGH COMPRESSION ENGINES ADD 'H' BEFORE 'E' SUFFIX

[2] : CALIFORNIAN SPEC. ADD 'C' BETWEEN 'U' & 'E' SUFFIXES

[3] : L.H.D. ADD LETTER 'L' AFTER CHASSIS NUMBER

[3] : OVERDRIVE ADD LETTER 'O' AFTER CHASSIS NUMBER